Digging Numbers

ENCYCLOPÆDIA BRITANNICA EDUCATIONAL CORPORATION

Mathematics in Context is a comprehensive curriculum for the middle grades. It was developed in collaboration with the Wisconsin Center for Education Research, School of Education, University of Wisconsin–Madison and the Freudenthal Institute at the University of Utrecht, The Netherlands, with the support of National Science Foundation Grant No. 9054928.

National Science Foundation

Opinions expressed are those of the authors
and not necessarily those of the Foundation

The *Mathematics in Context* Development Team

Mathematics in Context is a comprehensive curriculum for the middle grades. The National Science Foundation funded the National Center for Research in Mathematical Sciences Education at the University of Wisconsin–Madison to develop and field-test the materials from 1991 through 1996. The Freudenthal Institute at the University of Utrecht in The Netherlands, as a subcontractor, collaborated with the University of Wisconsin–Madison on the development of the curriculum.

The initial version of *Digging Numbers* was developed by Jan de Lange and Anton Roodhardt. It was adapted for use in American schools by Margaret A. Pligge, Aaron N. Simon, James A. Middleton, and Beth R. Cole.

National Center for Research in Mathematical Sciences Education Staff

Thomas A. Romberg
Director

Joan Daniels Pedro
Assistant to the Director

Gail Burrill
Coordinator
Field Test Materials

Margaret R. Meyer
Coordinator
Pilot Test Materials

Mary Ann Fix
Editorial Coordinator

Sherian Foster
Editorial Coordinator

James A. Middleton
Pilot Test Coordinator

Margaret A. Pligge
First Edition Coordinator

Project Staff

Jonathan Brendefur
Laura J. Brinker
James Browne
Jack Burrill
Rose Byrd
Peter Christiansen
Barbara Clarke
Doug Clarke
Beth R. Cole

Fae Dremock
Jasmina Milinkovic
Kay Schultz
Mary C. Shafer
Julia A. Shew
Aaron N. Simon
Marvin Smith
Stephanie Z. Smith
Mary S. Spence
Kathleen Steele

Freudenthal Institute Staff

Jan de Lange
Director

Els Feijs
Coordinator

Martin van Reeuwijk
Coordinator

Project Staff

Mieke Abels
Nina Boswinkel
Frans van Galen
Koeno Gravemeijer
Marja van den Heuvel-Panhuizen
Jan Auke de Jong
Vincent Jonker
Ronald Keijzer

Martin Kindt
Jansie Niehaus
Nanda Querelle
Anton Roodhardt
Leen Streefland
Adri Treffers
Monica Wijers
Astrid de Wild

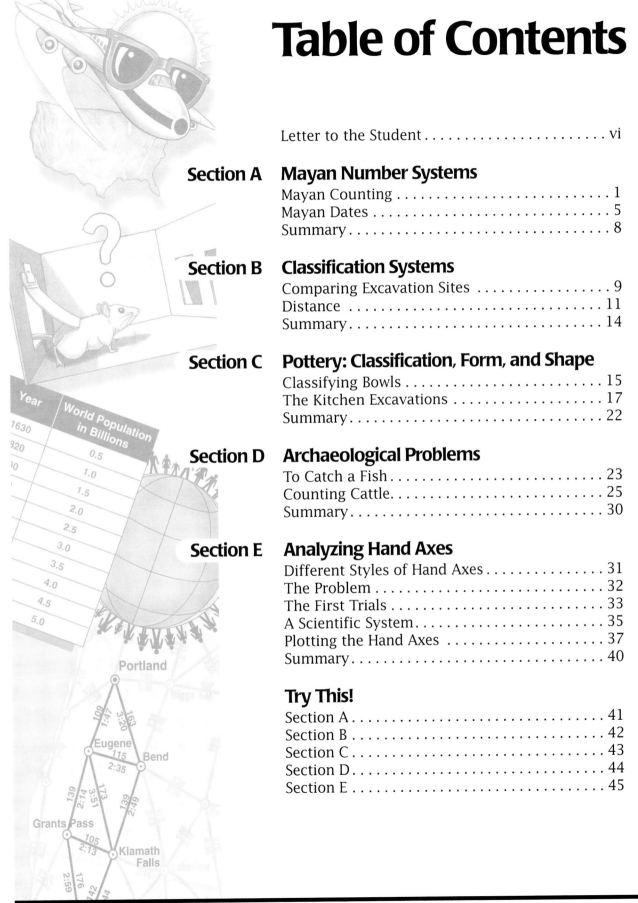

Table of Contents

Dear Student,

Welcome to *Digging Numbers.*

If you were an archaeologist, what do you think you would spend most of your time doing? Do you think you would be digging for bones and valuable artifacts or unearthing an ancient tomb?

Actually, archaeologists spend a lot of time doing math! An archaeologist's goal is to answer questions about ancient civilizations, such as How did these people live? How is this civilization similar to another civilization?

In this unit, you will study the base-20 number system of the Maya in order to understand how their calendar system worked. Once you understand the Mayan calendar system, you will decode dates of important events that the Maya recorded in stone carvings.

You will also learn a method for comparing various excavation sites in order to determine how similar they are. This method involves dividing the artifacts found at each site into groups, finding the percent for each group, and then finding the "distance" between the sites.

It is important to archaeologists to classify objects that they find at excavation sites. In this unit, you will classify objects by recording whether an object has a particular characteristic and by measuring and recording the dimensions of objects. You will also use different kinds of graphs to classify and compare objects.

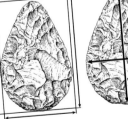

We hope you enjoy applying your mathematical knowledge to solving archaeological problems in *Digging Numbers.*

Sincerely,

The Mathematics in Context Development Team

A. MAYAN NUMBER SYSTEMS

Mayan Counting

El Castillo is the principal pyramid temple of Chichén Itzá, one of the largest of the Mayan cities. It is in present day Yucatán, Mexico. Large-scale archaeological excavation and restoration work has been done on all the major buildings found at this site.

The ancient Mayan civilization lasted for more than 2,000 years (1000 B.C.–A.D. 1500). Experts regard this civilization as having been extremely advanced. The Mayan civilization occupied the entire Yucatán Peninsula in Mexico, all of Guatemala and Belize, and parts of Honduras and El Salvador. Descendants of the Maya live in this region today; many still speak a Mayan language. Below is a map showing the region of Mayan culture.

1. Use **Student Activity Sheet 1** to estimate the size of the area of Mayan culture in square kilometers.

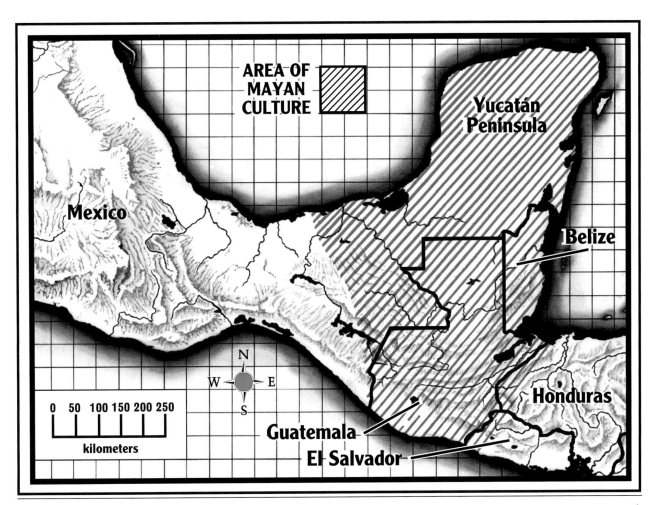

AREA OF MAYAN CULTURE

Yucatán Peninsula

Mexico

Belize

0 50 100 150 200 250
kilometers

N
W E
S

Guatemala

El Salvador

Honduras

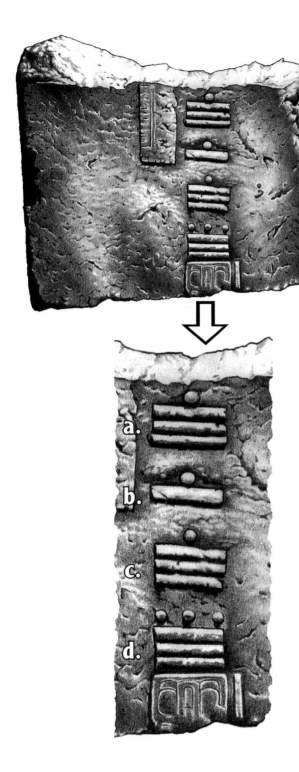

Mayan culture was advanced in terms of technology, science, and mathematics. One of the Maya's greatest achievements in mathematics was the development of a *positional number system* and the symbolic representation of the number zero, ⊖.

The stone block pictured on the left was found near the ruins of an ancient temple in Mexico. A column of numbers is carved on one side of the stone block.

Archaeologists can easily translate these numbers because the Maya used simple bar-and-dot notation. In this system,

stands for 4   and   stands for 7.

2. What are the four numbers labeled a, b, c, and d carved into the stone block on the left?

3. Using Mayan bar-and-dot notation, draw pictures of the following numbers:

    a. 2

    b. 8

    c. 14

    d. 10

For the number 20, the Maya could have used four bars.

They could have continued writing numbers in this way, with bars, indefinitely.

4. Why do you think it was critical for the Maya to invent a symbol for zero?

The number system that you use everyday, the decimal system, is a positional system. In a positional system, the position of a digit has a specific meaning. For example, a 1 can mean "one," but it can also mean "ten" (as the 1 in 12) or "one hundred" (as the 1 in 143). In our system, which is based on ten, moving a digit one position to the left multiplies its value by 10.

The Maya also used a positional system, but they based their number system on the number 20, not 10. The number 19 was written with a group of four dots (ones) and three bars (fives). Instead of using four bars to write the number 20, the Maya used a new position. The illustrations of Mayan numbers in this section show each position enclosed by a box so that it is easier to see the different positions.

17 was written: **19 was written:**

21 was written: **23 was written:**   **25 was written:**

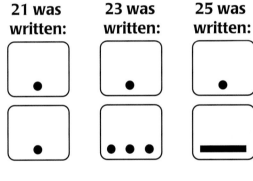

5. a. For the number 21, what does the dot in the upper box mean?

    b. Why do you think the Maya chose 20 as the base of their number system?

    c. Draw the numbers 20, 24, 39, and 40 using Mayan bar-and-dot notation.

6. What numbers are represented by **a** and **b** pictured on the right?

a.   **b.**

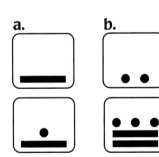

7. Draw the Mayan symbols for the following numbers:

    a. 200   **b.** 287   **c.** 399

8. Explain why the Maya needed a new position to write 400.

9. Explain why the number shown on the right represents 888.

10. What is the largest Mayan number possible using only three positions?

888 =   **? =**

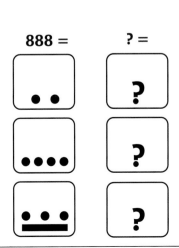

Here is a helpful way to determine the value of a Mayan number.

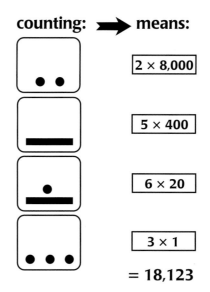

counting: ➤ means:

$2 \times 8{,}000$

5×400

6×20

3×1

$= 18{,}123$

11. Why is the Mayan number system called a "base-20" system?

**The Hindu-Arabic System
(Our System)**

The Mayan System

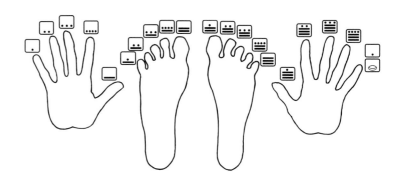

12. How does the Mayan number system compare to our number system?

The stone block that we looked at earlier is not four separate numbers; it is one large number with four positions.

13. What is the number carved into the stone block shown on the right?

Mayan Dates

The Maya wrote using picture symbols that archaeologists call *hieroglyphs,* or *glyphs* for short. The Maya also used glyphs to tell the date. On the right is a picture of the formal, long way that the Maya wrote important dates. In addition to showing an exact count of all the days from the beginning of the Mayan calendar, these glyphs include information on the names of the day and month, the god associated with the day, as well as information about the moon.

baktun
144,000 days

tun
360 days

kin
1 day

katun
7,200 days

uinal
20 days

Archaeologists have found that the five glyphs labeled in the picture on the right are the key to figuring out dates. Each glyph represents a different number of days. The glyph marked *kin* stands for "day," the basic unit of the Mayan calendar.

14. a. How many kins equal 1 uinal?

   b. How many uinals equal 1 tun?

   c. How many tuns equal 1 katun?

   d. How many katuns equal 1 baktun?

The Maya used a bar-and-dot notation with the glyphs, showing dates similar to the way that they showed numbers. For example, three days was represented by three dots in front of the kin glyph.

kin

3 days

15. Make a drawing for 17 days (your glyph does not have to be precise).

The uinal is 20 kins (days), a period of time similar to our month. On the right are the Mayan glyphs that represent 20 days. Notice that the kin in the example on the right has no bars or dots. Its value is zero.

uinal   **kin**

16. Make drawings for 22 days and 82 days.

A *tun,* pictured on the right, has a unique value: it represents only 18 uinals, or 360 days. It is thought that the Maya departed from the base-20 system in this position so that the tun would have 360 days (instead of 400) and be closer in length to the 365-day solar year.

tun **uinal** **kin**

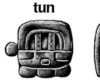

17. Make drawings for 359 days and 361 days.

The date on the right includes the katun glyph, the glyph for 7,200 days.

katun **tun** **uinal** **kin**

18. How many days are represented by the above glyphs?

19. Explain why the glyph on the right represents 1,440,000 days.

The glyphs shown below are from the stone carving shown on page 5.

baktun **katun** **tun** **uinal** **kin**

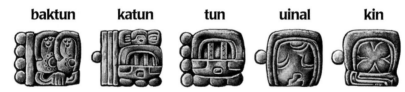

20. Explain why these glyphs represent 1,412,661 days.

The ruins of the ancient Mayan city Yaxchilán are famous for their many stone carvings. Some of these carvings record important events in the life of the ruler Bird-Jaguar III. The carving above shows Bird-Jaguar preparing to battle his enemy, Jeweled-Skull. Bird-Jaguar is shown with his wife, 6-Sky-Ahau. The row of glyphs on the bottom of page 6 show the date that Bird-Jaguar fought Jeweled-Skull, day number 1,412,661.

Shown below is a Mayan date from a different carving at Yaxchilán. It records the day on which Bird-Jaguar III became the king of Yaxchilán.

21. a. How many days does this date represent?

    b. Was Bird-Jaguar king of Yaxchilán when he fought Jeweled-Skull?

22. Explain why the Mayan date system is not a perfect base-20 system.

Summary

In this section, you studied the Mayan positional number system. The Mayan counting system is a *base-20* system. The Maya counted to 19 (using dots and bars) before moving to the next position. In our *base-10* system, we count to nine before moving to the next position.

The Maya recorded important dates on stone tablets. They combined date-counting with pictorial glyphs. The Mayan date-counting system was slightly different than a base-20 system, as shown below.

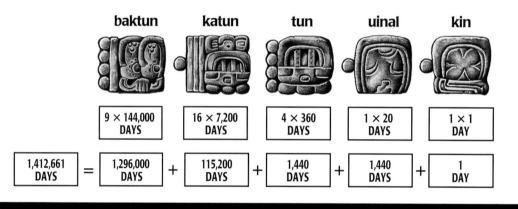

baktun	katun	tun	uinal	kin
9 × 144,000 DAYS	16 × 7,200 DAYS	4 × 360 DAYS	1 × 20 DAYS	1 × 1 DAY

1,412,661 DAYS	=	1,296,000 DAYS	+	115,200 DAYS	+	1,440 DAYS	+	1,440 DAYS	+	1 DAY

Summary Questions

23. How many days old are you? Show your calculations, and write your age using Mayan glyphs.

24. What makes our calendar system difficult to work with?

Comparing Excavation Sites

Archaeologists carefully excavate and catalog everything that they find at an excavation site. They try to relate the pieces they find in order to understand the ancient civilization. Every excavation adds new pieces to the puzzle.

Comparing one excavation site to another can give archaeologists information about how different ancient peoples lived. For example, if two sites contain the same kinds of things, this can show that the people who lived at these sites had similar lifestyles.

Peter Robinson, an archaeologist, uses the following method to sort and compare the remains from different excavation sites.

First, he divides the excavated remains into different classes:

> 1) HUMAN BONES
> 2) ANIMAL BONES
> 3) POTTERY
> 4) CLOTHING
> 5) MISCELLANEOUS

Other classifications are possible, depending on what is being studied and the type of excavation.

1. What other kinds of classifications can you think of?

The results from excavation site A (in weight) are as follows:

> 10% HUMAN BONES
> 25% ANIMAL BONES
> 35% POTTERY
> 20% CLOTHING
> 10% MISCELLANEOUS

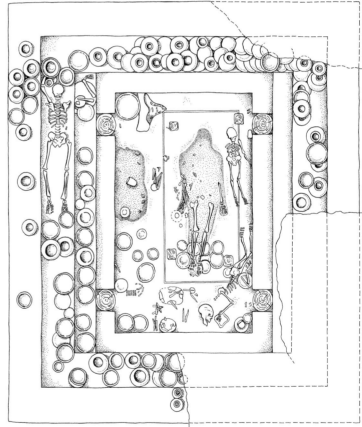

This is an archaeologist's drawing of an excavated Mayan tomb. It records the position of everything in the tomb when the archaeologists discovered it. The round shapes are pieces of pottery. This grave site is at the early Mayan center of Kaminalijuyú, near present-day Guatemala City, Guatemala. Like many Mayan tombs, it is filled with valuable artifacts. This tomb contained a headdress carved from jadeite.

Altogether five excavation sites were explored with the following results:

Excavation Site	% Human Bones	% Animal Bones	% Pottery	% Clothing	% Miscellaneous
A	10	25	35	20	10
B	0	40	30	25	5
C	5	10	25	40	20
D	25	25	25	15	10
E	0	10	25	40	25

2. **a.** In which excavation site(s) did the archaeologists find no human bones?

   b. Which excavation site had the highest percent of animal bones?

3. **a.** Draw a bar graph for each excavation site to show the percent of excavated remains in each category.

   b. Based upon the bar graphs that you drew for part **a,** which two excavation sites look the most similar? Explain.

The Mayan grave sites on the island of Jaina contained a special treasure: hundreds of well-preserved clay figurines showing the Maya as they worked and dressed.

On the left, a Mayan warrior wears padded armor to protect him from stone-tipped arrows.

On the right, a finely dressed Mayan woman is weaving at her loom. Her pet parrots are on the floor by her feet.

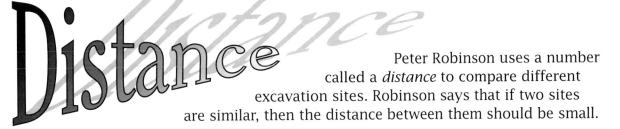

Peter Robinson uses a number called a *distance* to compare different excavation sites. Robinson says that if two sites are similar, then the distance between them should be small.

To find the distance between sites A and B, Peter first finds the differences in the percents of the remains found.

	% Human Bones	% Animal Bones	% Pottery	% Clothing	% Miscellaneous
A	10	25	35	20	10
B	0	40	30	25	5
A − B	10 − 0 = 10	25 − 40 = −15	35 − 30 = 5	20 − 25 = −5	10 − 5 = 5

To find the total distance between sites A and B, Peter could add these differences (10 + −15 + 5 + −5 + 5).

4. a. What is the sum of the differences between sites A and B? Is this number a good description of the distance between sites A and B? Explain.

b. In which situation would you want the distance between two sites to be zero?

Because Peter wants the distance between two sites to be small when the sites are similar, he adds another step—he finds the absolute values of the differences before adding them.

The *absolute value* of a number is its distance from zero on a number line. For example, the absolute value of −5 is 5 because −5 is 5 units from zero.

Vertical lines on the left and right sides of a number indicate the absolute value of the number. For example, the absolute value of −3, which equals 3, can be written as |−3|. Notice that |−3| = 3, and |3| = 3.

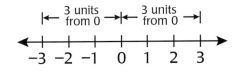

When Peter adds the absolute values of the differences, as shown below, the distance between sites A and B is 40. This can be written as d(A, B) = 40.

|A − B|	**|10| = 10**	**|−15| = 15**	**|5| = 5**	**|−5| = 5**	**|5| = 5**

5. a. Use Peter's definition of distance to compute the distance between each pair of excavation sites A–E. Make a table like the one on the right for your answers.

Site	A	B	C	D	E
A	0	40			
B	40	0			
C			0		
D				0	
E					0

b. Why are there zeros along the diagonal of the table?

c. Which excavation sites are close together? Which are far apart? How can you tell?

6. What is the maximum distance possible between two excavation sites?

7. How might this table be helpful to archaeologists?

Four other sites were excavated later:

• In excavation site F, there were equal percents in all five classes: human bones, animal bones, pottery, clothing, and miscellaneous.

• Excavation site G yielded almost nothing but pottery (95%) and some clothing remains (5%).

• In excavation site H, there were only human bones.

• In excavation site I, archaeologists found equal percents of human and animal bones and just 10% each for the other classes.

8. a. Make a bar graph for each new site (F, G, H, and I). Describe what these sites might have been during Mayan times.

b. Now make a distance table similar to the one shown above for sites F, G, H, and I. What can you tell from this table?

c. How does the information in the table compare to that in the bar graphs?

In 1946, the excavation site at Bonampak revealed three chambers filled with beautiful, well-preserved Mayan murals. Above is a section of a mural, showing a procession of musicians and men dressed in fantastic animal costumes, one of which appears to have the claws of a lobster.

The picture above shows Mayan stone carvings of nearly 400 masks that decorate the front of the Palace of the Masks at Kabah.

One archaeologist was making a distance table for sites P and Q. Unfortunately, a power surge destroyed the computer file that contained the only copy of the table. She was able to remember all but four of the numbers. She also remembered that the percent of human bones at site P and the percent of animal bones at site Q were the same. By looking at the report summary she had filed, she found that d(P, Q) = 46.

9. a. Looking only at the values in row P in the table below, determine the largest possible value for the percent of human bones at site P.

   b. In your notebook, copy the following table and fill in the missing percents.

	% Human Bones	% Animal Bones	% Pottery	% Refuse Matter	% Clothing	% Stone Tools
P		10		23	35	12
Q	15		25	17	18	

Summary

In this section, you looked at the percents of remains found at excavation sites. First you used bar graphs to show the percent of the total remains that were found in each category for a single site and to compare two sites.

Next you used distance as a way to compare different sites. To find the distance between two sites, you added the absolute values of the differences between the percents for each category. The more similar two sites are, the smaller the distance between them. If two sites are identical, the distance between them is zero.

Summary Questions

10. Why do you think Peter Robinson uses the percents of objects at a site instead of the numbers of objects to report his findings?

11. Suppose archaeologists excavate your school in the year 2345. Describe what they might find, and contrast it with what they might find if they were to excavate a shopping mall.

These Mayan ruins are at Chichén Itzá. Archaeologists think that this building was an observatory. The architecture of this building reveals the Maya's knowledge of important astronomical events. A spiral staircase in the center of the building leads to a small, windowed chamber. At each equinox, windows in the chamber frame the setting sun and the setting moon.

Classifying Bowls

In the previous section, you compared artifacts found at different excavation sites. Now you will examine the artifacts found at one excavation site.

Broken fragments, called shards, from a number of bowls were found during an excavation. Some of them had decorations, some were plain, some were glazed, and some had handles. A collection of complete and partial bowls was put together from the pieces. The archaeologists wanted to organize this collection and needed a system for classifying the different bowls.

1. What are some ways to classify and organize pottery in addition to whether or not the pottery has decorations, a glaze, or handles?

with or without handles

cylindrical or not

decorated or not

glazed or not

One archaeologist decides to classify the bowls according to the four characteristics shown on the left. For each characteristic he uses a "1" to indicate that the characteristic is present and a "0" to show that the characteristic is not present. He classifies six bowls according to these characteristics:

	Handles	Cylindrical	Decorated	Glazed
Bowl A	1	0	1	0
Bowl B	0	1	0	0
Bowl C	1	0	1	1
Bowl D	0	1	0	1
Bowl E	0	1	1	1
Bowl F	0	0	0	1

2. Which cylindrical bowl has no handles, is not decorated, but is glazed? Draw a picture of this bowl.

3. Bowls that differ in only one characteristic are considered close together. Find which bowls are close together.

4. How can you find the distance between two bowls? Use your method to find the distance between bowls A and B.

5. Draw a distance table for bowls A–F.

6. How is your method for finding the distance between two bowls different than Peter Robinson's method for finding the distance between two excavation sites?

7. How many different types of bowls are possible using only the four characteristics given above?

8. How many different types of bowls are possible if you use five characteristics?

Activity

The Kitchen Excavations

A group of archaeologists excavated an ancient village and found what appeared to be four kitchens. The drawings on the right show the pottery that was found in each kitchen.

Kitchen A

9. Using **Student Activity Sheets 2** and **3,** devise a system for classifying the pottery in the four kitchens. Then use your system to describe how the four kitchens relate to each other. Organize the data any way you want, but be prepared to explain your methods.

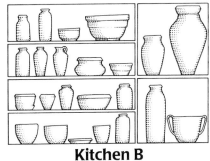

Kitchen B

Kitchen C

Kitchen D

a.

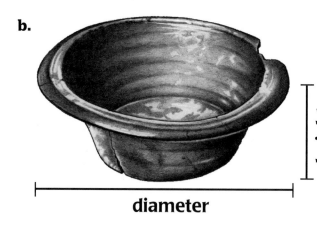

diameter

Archaeologists are interested in the shape of pottery because it may tell something about how a piece was used.

10. Explain how you could use the height and diameter of a container to classify it.

Chris Webster, an archaeologist, uses the following classification system for containers:

Jar: a container with a narrowing at the neck whose diameter is less than its height

Bowl: a neckless container whose height is between its diameter and one-third of its diameter

Dish: a shallow container having a height of between one-seventh and one-third of its diameter

Plate: a shallow container whose height is not greater than one-seventh its diameter

11. Which of Mr. Webster's names would you give to each of the three containers shown on the left?

12. Rewrite Mr. Webster's categories using the radius instead of the diameter.

b.

diameter

c.

diameter

The three vessels shown above were collected from excavations in Dorset, United Kingdom.

Professor Maria Olaya-Davis was invited to give a speech about Chris Webster's classification system at the annual archaeology convention. In her presentation, she described a plate in the following way:

$$\text{height} \leq \tfrac{2}{7} \text{ radius}$$

13. How did she get this formula?

Then she showed a picture and graph to demonstrate that a particular container is a plate. She said, "The point P shows that this is a plate."

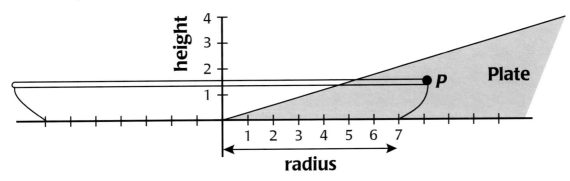

14. a. Estimate the coordinates of point P.

   b. How do the coordinates of point P show that the container is a plate?

15. Explain how you could use the following graph to show whether or not a container is a plate.

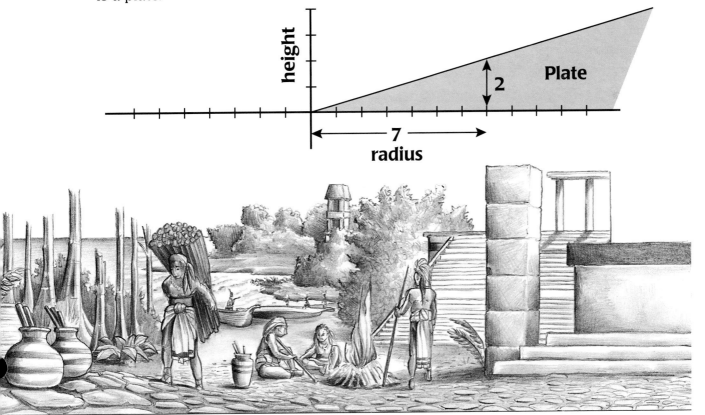

Next, Professor Olaya-Davis showed her mathematical formula for a dish:

$$\tfrac{2}{7} \text{ radius} \leq \text{height} \leq \tfrac{2}{3} \text{ radius}$$

16. a. Draw a graph for a dish, similar to Professor Olaya-Davis's plate graph.

    b. Draw a picture of a dish on your graph just as Professor Olaya-Davis drew a plate.

17. a. Find the formula for a bowl.

    b. Make a graph that shows this formula.

    c. Draw a picture of a bowl on your graph.

18. Find the formula and draw a graph for a jar. Include a picture of a jar in your graph.

After attending Professor Olaya-Davis's presentation, Dr. Allison Laws had a clever idea. She designed the chart on the right for classifying containers.

19. Explain how Dr. Laws's container classification model works.

20. Use **Student Activity Sheet 4** and Dr. Laws's model to classify the six containers pictured below on the right.

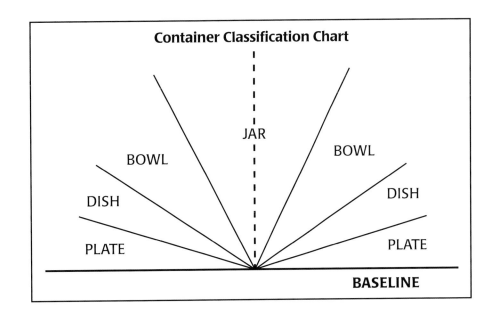

Container Classification Chart

JAR

BOWL   BOWL

DISH   DISH

PLATE   PLATE

BASELINE

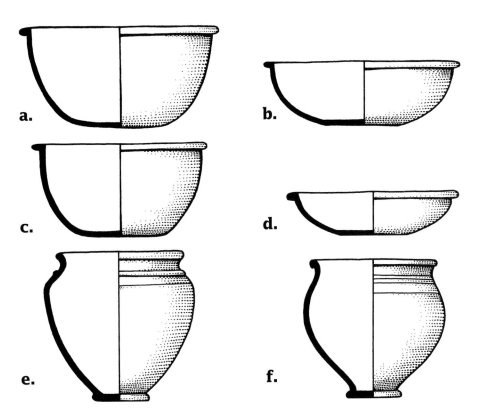

a.

b.

c.

d.

e.

f.

These containers are drawn in a style used by archaeologists. The right side of the drawing shows the outside, and the left side shows a cross-section with the heavy black line showing the thickness of the sides.

Summary

In this section, you classified pottery at an excavation site using four categories: whether or not a piece has a handle, whether it is cylindrical or not, whether it has decoration, and whether it is glazed. This classification system uses a "1" if the characteristic is present and a "0" if it is not.

You also classified pottery by writing rules or formulas that describe characteristics. You used the formulas to create pictures and graphs, which could then be used to determine whether or not a container is a jar, bowl, dish, or plate.

Summary Questions

21. a. Describe some objects other than pottery that you can classify by making a list of several possible characteristics and writing a "1" if the characteristic is present and a "0" if it is not. Explain why you would use this method of classification for these objects.

b. Describe some objects other than pottery that you could classify by using formulas. Explain why you would use this method of classification for these objects.

22. The following picture shows how to classify athletic shoes. Describe this classification system.

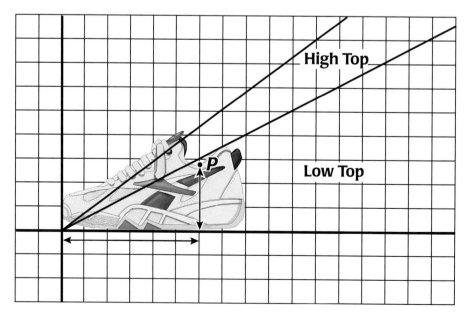

To Catch a Fish

Some archaeologists study ancient plant and animal life. They want to find out how the plants and animals that lived long ago compare to those alive today.

In the 1980s, about 5,000 fish bones were found in a dry lake bed in Denmark. Archaeologists determined that they belonged to fish who lived in about 3000 B.C. The archaeologists who studied the remains asked, "Was the aquatic life in this ancient lake similar to that in our modern lakes?"

1. Why might it be important to know whether the ancient lake had life similar to modern lakes?

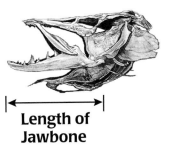

Length of Jawbone

The archaeologists chose to focus their attention on the northern pike (*Esox lucius*). No complete skeletons of the pike were found. The jawbone was the part that was most easily recognized, so the archaeologists used jawbones in their study.

Length of Jawbone

⟵——————— **Length of Fish** ———————⟶

The following is a list of the sizes (in millimeters) of all of the ancient pike jawbones that were found.

73	32	65	71	66	45	55	54	48	77	39	60	62	42
86	58	74	66	69	52	55	63	61	77	79	84	80	44
77	74	83	83	59	34	73	91	63	71	72	59	64	69
74	29	88	35	74	79	63	54	77	89	81	53	48	69
87	65	49	58	60	38	78	77	73	91	62	51	87	67

2. Organize the data given above and, in a few sentences, describe the ancient jawbone data.

To compare the ancient fish to modern fish, the archaeologists measured fish caught in a lake close to the archaeological site. The lengths of the modern northern pike and their corresponding jawbone lengths are listed below on the right.

3. Organize the data given on the right and, in a few sentences, describe the modern fish data.

4. Were the ancient fish similar to the modern fish? Use the data on the ancient and modern fish and statistical summaries to support your answer. You may also use a graphing calculator and **Student Activity Sheets 5–8.**

5. If an ancient fish had a jawbone length of 48 millimeters, how long do you think the fish was? Explain how you found your answer and any assumptions that you may have made.

Modern Northern Pike	
Jawbone (in mm)	Length (in mm)
110	760
85	602
88	612
101	743
66	479
77	543
80	588
97	661
101	708
111	751
96	659
80	559
83	601
75	539
92	643
94	656
87	610
72	515
90	630
106	729

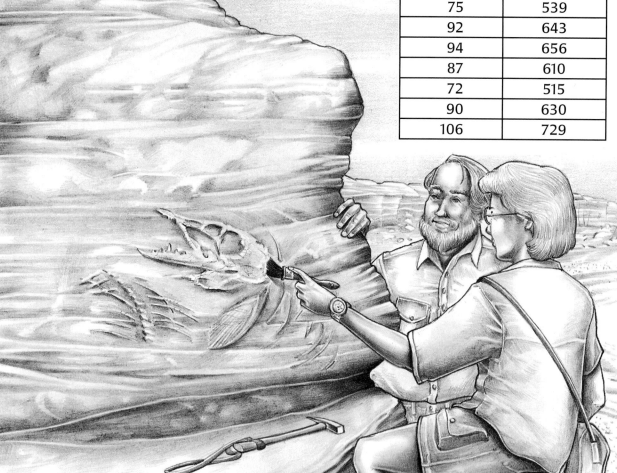

Counting Cattle

Professor Paludan, an archaeologist interested in ancient African civilizations, is completing excavations at the site of an ancient settlement in Ethiopia. Among the finds are many pottery shards and animal bones. Many of the bones he has uncovered are cattle femurs (thighbones). Professor Paludan hopes these will give him some valuable clues about the people who lived at this site.

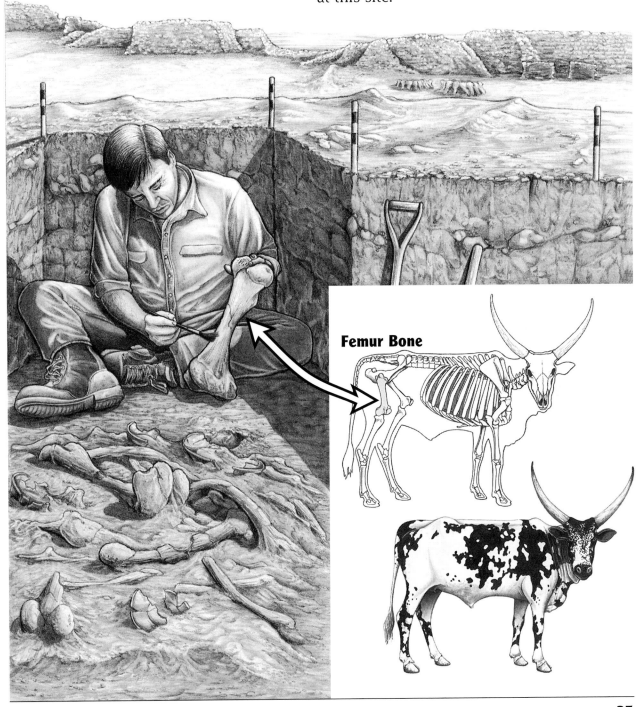

Femur Bone

Case 1

Professor Paludan has organized the femurs into right and left leg bones. With careful measurements, he has determined that some of the bones are pairs from the same animal.

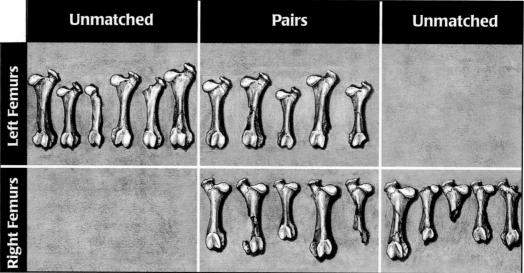

	Unmatched	Pairs	Unmatched
Left Femurs			
Right Femurs			

From this collection of femurs, Professor Paludan believes that he can estimate how many cattle were kept at the ancient settlement. Furthermore, he believes that he can estimate the number of people who lived at the settlement based on the number of cattle they kept.

6. a. How might you estimate how many people lived at a site if you know the total number of cattle found at the site?

b. If you make this kind of prediction, what are some problems you could encounter?

One of Professor Paludan's assistants looked at the bones and suggested that there were 16 cattle.

7. a. How do you think the assistant made this estimate?

b. Develop a formula that Professor Paludan's assistant could have used to find the number of cattle based on the number of femurs.

c. Do you think that 16 is a reasonable estimate for the number of cattle? Why or why not?

The bones that Professor Paludan found came from a type of cattle still raised by the modern people of Ethiopia. These cattle can be brown, black, white, or speckled, and they can survive conditions of extreme heat, drought, and disease.

Case 2

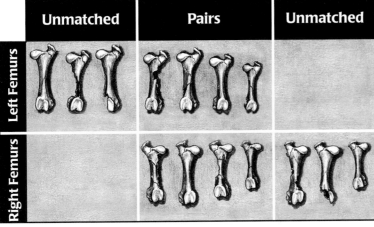

Case 3

8. a. Use your formula to determine the total number of cattle in cases 2 and 3 pictured on the left.

  b. Explain your results from part **a.** Do you think the settlements represented by cases 2 and 3 actually had the same number of cattle?

Professor Paludan is not satisfied with his results using this formula. He would like to create a new formula.

9. What factors should a new formula take into account?

In order to choose an appropriate formula for finding the total number of cattle at a site, Professor Paludan asks Professor Krantz for advice. Professor Krantz explains that you must also take into consideration the number of missing cattle, or the number of cattle that were kept at the settlement but for which no bones were found during the excavation. Professor Krantz uses the formula shown on the right to find the number of missing cattle at an excavation site.

$$M = \frac{L^2 + R^2}{2P}$$

M: Missing number of cattle

L: Number of single unmatched left femurs

R: Number of single unmatched right femurs

P: Number of pairs of femurs

10. a. Use Professor Krantz's formula to find the number of missing cattle for cases 2 and 3 on page 27.

b. Does Professor Krantz's formula address the concerns you listed in problem **9?**

One way to test a formula is to apply it to special cases. Two special cases are as follows:

- No cattle femurs were found at the site.

- Only pairs of cattle femurs were found at the site.

11. a. List any other special cases that you can think of.

b. What happens if you use Professor Krantz's formula for each special case?

The hardy African long-horned cattle have an ancient relationship with the cattle-herding people of Africa. They appear in cave paintings that were made at least 4,000 years ago by Stone Age cattle-herders in the Tassili region of the central Saharan uplands.

Professor De Vries is a colleague of Professor Paludan. She believes that you shouldn't always trust a formula. Bones can disappear for a variety of reasons. To demonstrate her point, she removes one bone from the table while Professor Paludan is out of the room. When Professor Paludan returns, she says, "Hey, your calculations are all wrong!"

12. a. Calculate the number of missing cattle from the collection shown on the right (case 1) using Professor Kranz's formula from page 28.

b. Take away one bone from the collection and calculate the number of missing cattle.

c. Does your answer to part **b** change if you remove a bone from a different category? If so, which type of bone changes the answer for the number of missing cattle the most? Explain.

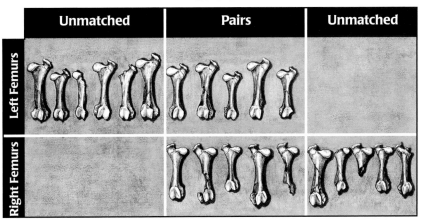

Case 1

	Unmatched	Pairs	Unmatched
Left Femurs			
Right Femurs			

Four thousand years ago, these painted wooden models of African long-horned cattle and their herdsmen were placed into the tomb of an Egyptian nobleman. To the ancient civilizations in Africa, cattle provided more than milk and meat. Harnessed cattle pulled plows through the farm fields and sledges of stone blocks to building sites.

Summary

In this section, you analyzed fish and cattle bones in order to learn more about animal life during ancient times. To see whether a fish population had changed over time, you compared ancient fish bones to the bones of modern fish.

You then looked at cattle bones from excavation sites. First, you developed a formula to find the number of cattle based on the number of femurs. You then worked with a different formula to determine the number of missing cattle for an excavation site. Both of the formulas that you worked with had strengths and weaknesses.

Summary Questions

Professor De Vries showed her colleague Professor Paludan the formula on the right and suggested that he use it to find the number of missing cattle at a site.

$$M = \frac{L \cdot R}{P}$$

13. **a.** Use Professor De Vries's formula to find the numbers of missing cattle for case 1 on page 26 and for cases 2 and 3 on page 27.

    b. How does Professor De Vries's formula compare to Professor Krantz's formula on page 28? When do both formulas give the same answer?

14. Is the following statement true or false? Explain your answer.

    Professor Krantz's formula will always indicate that either the same number or more cattle were missing in a particular situation than Professor De Vries's formula will indicate.

Different Styles of Hand Axes

Hand axes from the Stone Age have been found all over the world. People used them for cutting the hides and meat from animals. Before the invention of metal blades, the stone hand ax was the sharpest and hardest edge available for cutting, chopping, and scraping.

No two hand axes are exactly the same. The shape and flaking pattern of a hand ax help an archaeologist determine which culture of ancient people made it. Shown below is one example of how someone made a hand ax during the Stone Age.

How the Stone Age Hand Ax Was Made

i. Break a large flake of flint from a rock.

ii. Roughly shape the rock with a stone hammer.

iii. Refine the rock with blows from a baton made of wood, stone, or antler.

iv. Trim the edge by pressure-flaking against a soft surface.

v. A few more touches produce a finished hand ax.

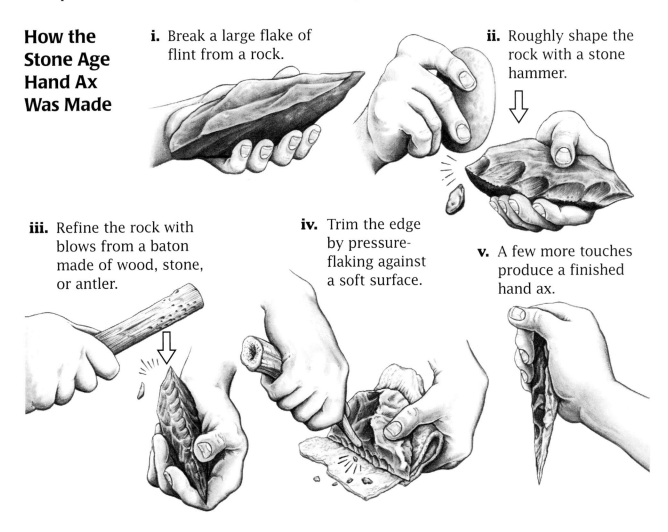

On **Student Activity Sheet 9,** an archaeologist's drawing of a hand ax from the Stone Age is shown. Archaeologists use drawings like this, showing different views (front, back, right, and left sides) of an object, to help them describe and catalog the items they find.

1. Label the views of the hand ax that are shown on **Student Activity Sheet 9.**

The Problem

An archaeologist visits a site, and the excavators show him some hand axes. He is able to look at the axes and tell which people made them and when they were made. One of the things he examines is the shape of each hand ax.

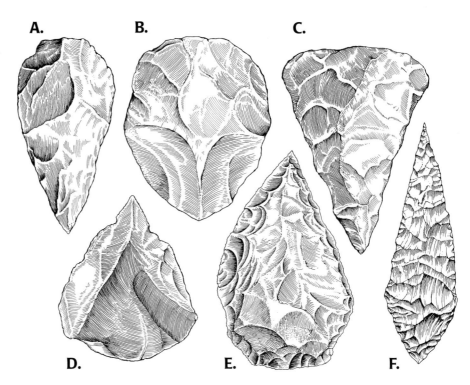

A. **B.** **C.**

D. **E.** **F.**

A selection of hand axes:
Axes A, B, C, and D are believed to have been made by Homo erectus people between 300,000 and 100,000 B.C. A more refined style is shown in E, believed to have been made by Homo sapiens neanderthalensis people between 100,000 and 35,000 B.C. The most refined style is shown by F, made by Homo sapiens sapiens, around 20,000 B.C.

2. Why do you think the shape is important?

3. Study the hand axes pictured above on the right and describe their shapes.

4. Study the hand ax shapes pictured below. If there were only two classes, heart-shaped and triangular, how would you classify the third ax?

heart-shaped

triangular

???

Of course, there can be more classes, but there will always be borderline cases or axes that do not fit nicely into a single category. The key is to develop a system of measuring and calculating that will distinguish between different types of hand axes.

The First Trials

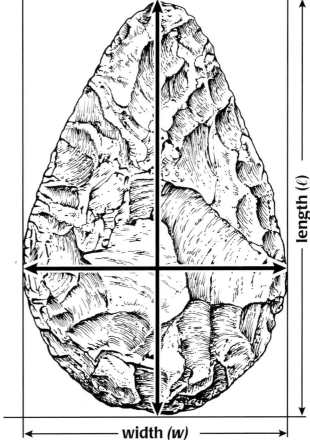

Many classification systems use measurements.

5. a. For the hand ax pictured on the right, measure the length (ℓ) and the width (w) in millimeters. Do you think your measurements are exact? Explain.

  b. What are some problems with using only length and width to classify an ax?

Archaeologists sometimes use length and width to calculate a single number that describes each ax.

6. a. Measure the length and width of each hand ax shown on **Student Activity Sheet 10.**

  b. Use the length and width of each hand ax to find one number that can be used to classify the hand ax. Explain your classification system.

Archaeologists sometimes use the ratio of the length to the width ($\frac{\ell}{w}$) to describe an ax.

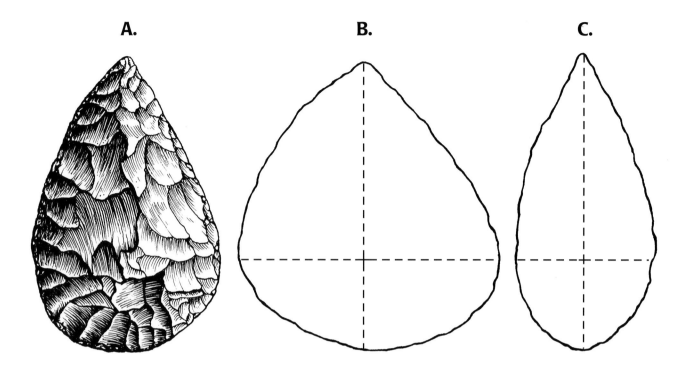

A.   **B.**   **C.**

7. **a.** What is the value of $\frac{\ell}{w}$ for ax A shown above?

   b. Compare the values of $\frac{\ell}{w}$ for axes A, B, and C, without measuring and calculating.

It is not possible to determine exact measurements. Measurements always have small errors.

   c. Suppose an archaeologist measures the length of an ax as 65 millimeters and the width as 43 millimeters, but her measurements may be off by as much as 1 millimeter. How big could $\frac{\ell}{w}$ actually be? How small?

8. **a.** Draw three different axes for which $\frac{\ell}{w} = 2.5$.

   b. How well do you think the ratio $\frac{\ell}{w}$ describes the shape of a hand ax?

A Scientific System

Bart Bordes, an archaeologist, offers another possible formula to use for classifying hand axes.

He makes four measurements:

ℓ: the length

w: the width

d: the distance between the line showing the widest part of the ax and the blunt end of the ax

h: the width of the ax at half the total length

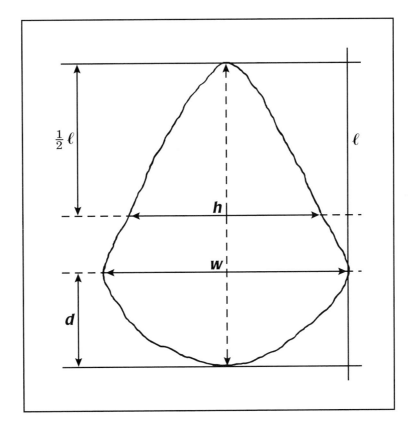

9. Find ℓ, w, d, and h for the hand ax pictured above.

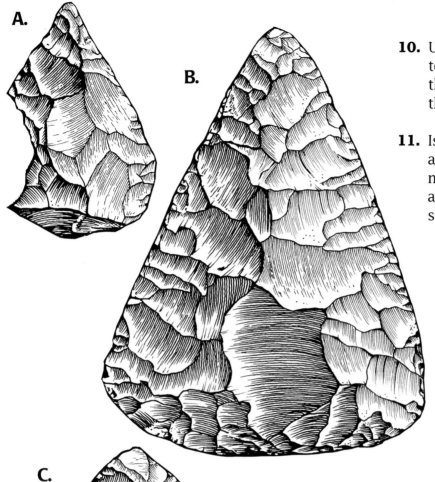

A.

B.

C.

10. Use **Student Activity Sheet 11** to find ℓ, w, d, and h for the three hand axes shown on the left.

11. Is it possible to find two axes that have the same measurements for ℓ, w, d, and h, but are different shapes? Why or why not?

   Archaeologists sometimes reduce the four measurements ℓ, w, d, and h to two numbers, x and y:

$$x = \frac{h}{w} \times 100$$

$$y = \frac{\ell}{d}$$

12. Determine x and y for the three hand axes shown on **Student Activity Sheet 11.**

13. In an archaeologist's report, a hand ax is described with $x = 64$ and $y = 3$.

   a. Draw a picture of a hand ax that could fit this description.

   b. Compare your drawing with those of others in your class. Do they all look the same?

   c. Do x and y provide enough information to determine the shape of an ax? Explain.

Plotting the Hand Axes

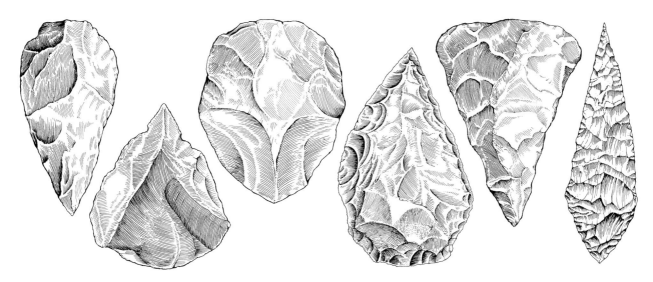

There are other ways to look at this classification problem.

Archaeologist Bart Bordes has a large collection of hand axes that he must classify. He wants to get a visual impression of the data. He plots points on a single graph, using the *x* and *y* values.

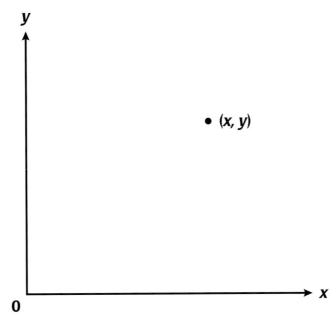

14. a. What do you think is the largest possible value of *y* for a hand ax? (Remember that $y = \frac{\ell}{d}$.) Explain.

b. Is 100 the largest possible value for *x*? (Remember that $x = \frac{h}{w} \times 100$.) Explain.

Bart Bordes plots the values for *x* and *y* for his large collection of hand axes. His graph is shown below and on **Student Activity Sheet 12.**

15. **a.** Describe some patterns that you notice in the graph.

   b. On **Student Activity Sheet 12,** add points for the three hand axes you measured for problem **12** on page 36. Label the points *A*, *B*, and *C*.

Mr. Bordes has identified four classes, or types, of hand axes in his collection. He had hoped that the graph would show four distinct areas.

16. Do you think that Mr. Bordes is satisfied with the results of his graph? Why or why not?

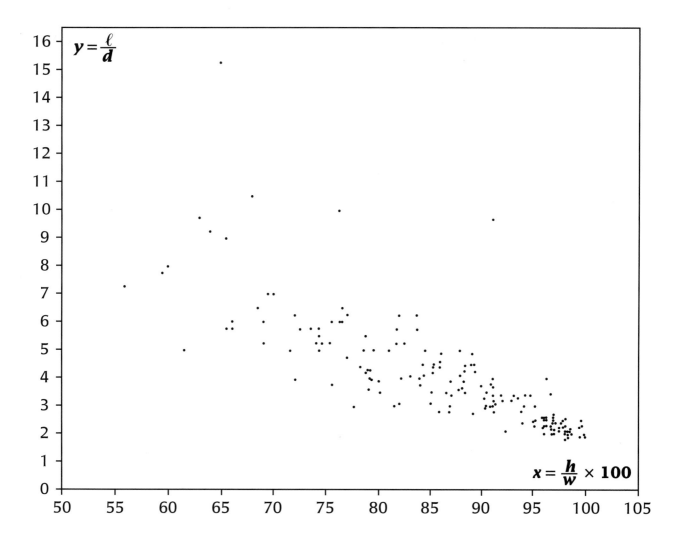

Mr. Bordes decides to ask for help from some experts on hand axes. They examine all the axes in his collection and divide them into the four classes.

Mr. Bordes then replaces each point on the graph with a symbol to indicate the class to which that ax belongs. His new graph is shown below.

17. Do you think that Mr. Bordes is satisfied with the results of his new graph? Why or why not?

18. Is there any ax that does not seem to be in the right place on the graph? If so, why do you think this might have happened?

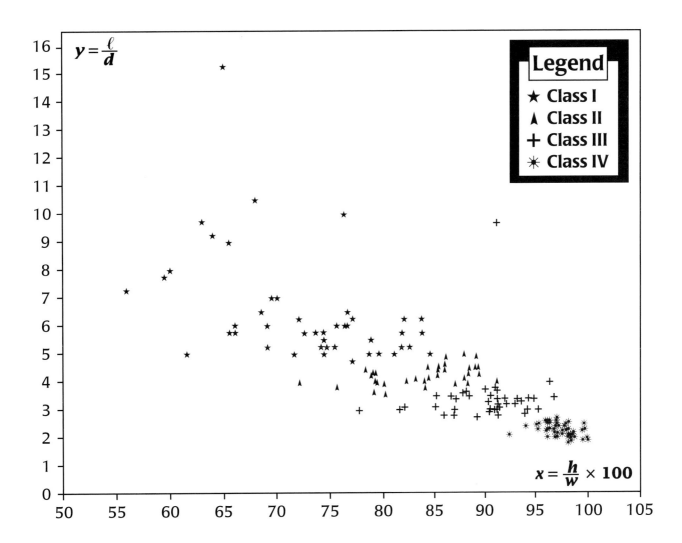

Bart Bordes's graph turned out even clearer than he expected. The distinctions between the classes can be made by three lines.

19. On **Student Activity Sheet 13,** draw three parallel lines that separate the four classes.

20. In which class does each ax that you measured for problem **12** on page 36 belong?

Summary

In this section, you analyzed the shapes of a variety of ancient hand axes. You measured the hand axes and used their measurements to classify them. One system of classification used only the length and width, but this system was not very precise; axes with the same length and width could look very different. A more precise system used four measurements (the length, the width, the distance between the width and the blunt end, and the width at the halfway point for the length) instead of two.

You then rewrote the four measurements for a hand ax as two numbers:

$$x = \frac{h}{w} \times 100$$

$$y = \frac{\ell}{d}$$

The two numbers (x, y) are convenient to work with because they can be graphed as data points. You then studied the graph of a collection of hand axes to identify any trends or clusters in the data.

Summary Questions

21. There are a variety of ways to classify hand axes. Look back through this section and find all the methods you have used. Give some advantages and disadvantages for each method of classification.

Section A. Mayan Number Systems

1. The Maya used a base-20 counting system. Which numbers are represented by the following notations?

   a. 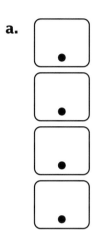   b.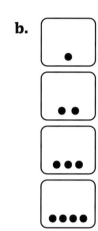

2. Represent 8,888 in Mayan notation.

3. Develop a base-12 counting system in which each bar represents a value of five and each dot represents a value of one.

   a. Draw 9.

   b. Draw 18.

   c. Draw 287.

   d. Which number is represented by the following notation?

   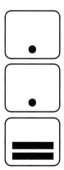

Section B. Classification Systems

Five excavation sites were explored with the following results:

Site	% Human Bones	% Animal Bones	% Pottery
A	0	70	30
B	5	5	90
C	10	60	30
D	70	30	0
E	10	10	80

1. Make a distance table to find the sites that are closest to each other.

2. Consider only sites B, C, and D in the above table. Which of these sites are closest to each other?

Section C. Pottery: Classification, Form, and Shape

1. Archaeologist Dr. Allison Laws designed the chart below for classifying containers.

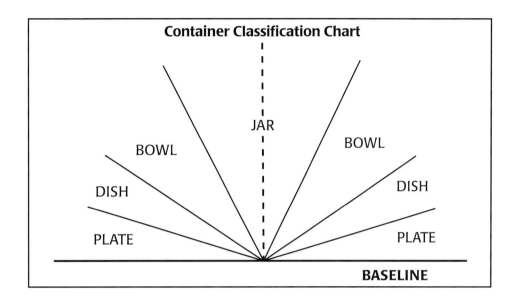

Use Dr. Laws's chart to design a bowl and a plate.

2. Mr. Webster calls an object a plate if it meets the following criterion: height $\leq \frac{2}{7}$ radius.

Dr. Jamison has a different rule for a plate: height $\leq \frac{3}{10}$ radius.

Who will classify more pottery as plates, Mr. Webster or Dr. Jamison? Explain.

Section D. Archaeological Problems

Professor Krantz created the formula shown below to find the number of missing cattle from the numbers of right, left, and paired femurs found at a site.

$$M = \frac{L^2 + R^2}{2P}$$

M: Missing number of cattle

L: Number of single unmatched left femurs

R: Number of single unmatched right femurs

P: Number of pairs of femurs

1. Compute the number of missing cattle in each of the following cases:

    a. $L = 2, P = 4, R = 2$

    b. $L = 20, P = 40, R = 20$

2. Find values for L, P, and R that result in a value for M that equals 100.

Professor De Vries devised the following formula to find the number of missing cattle:

$$M = \frac{L \bullet R}{P}$$

3. What is the difference in the number of cattle using Professor De Vries's and Professor Krantz's formulas for each of the cases below?

    a. $L = 200, P = 400, L = 200$

    b. $L = 100, P = 400, L = 300$

Section E. Analyzing Hand Axes

Archaeologist Bart Bordes came up with the idea of using the following four measurements to better classify hand axes:

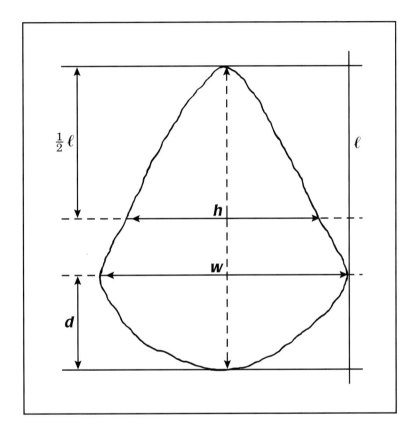

ℓ: the length

w: the width

d: the distance between the line showing the widest part of the ax and the blunt end of the ax

h: the width of the ax at half the total length

1. Draw a hand ax for which $\ell = 10$ cm, $w = 6$ cm, $d = 2$ cm, and $h = 3$ cm.

Bordes also devised the following formulas to find x and y values using the four measurements mentioned above:

$$x = \frac{h}{w} \times 100 \text{ and } y = \frac{\ell}{d}$$

2. Find x and y for the ax described in problem **1.**

3. Design an ax, different from the one in problem **1,** for which $x = 50$ and $y = 5$.

CREDITS

Cover

Design by Ralph Paquet/Encyclopædia Britannica Educational Corporation.

Collage by Koorosh Jamalpur/KJ Graphics.

Title Page

Paul Tucker/Encyclopædia Britannica Educational Corporation.

Illustrations

1 Phil Geib/Encyclopædia Britannica Educational Corporation; **2, 4, 5, 6 (top)** Paul Tucker/Encyclopædia Britannica Educational Corporation; **6 (bottom)** Phil Geib/Encyclopædia Britannica Educational Corporation; **7, 8 (top)** Paul Tucker/Encyclopædia Britannica Educational Corporation; **8 (bottom), 9** Phil Geib/Encyclopædia Britannica Educational Corporation; **10, 12** Paul Tucker/Encyclopædia Britannica Educational Corporation; **15, 16, 17 (bottom)** Phil Geib/Encyclopædia Britannica Educational Corporation; **17 (top), 18 (top)** Paul Tucker/Encyclopædia Britannica Educational Corporation; **18 (bottom), 19, 20, 22** Phil Geib/Encyclopædia Britannica Educational Corporation; **23** Jerome Gordon/Encyclopædia Britannica Educational Corporation; **24, 25, 26 (top)** Phil Geib/Encyclopædia Britannica Educational Corporation; **26 (bottom)** Jerome Gordon/Encyclopædia Britannica Educational Corporation; **27 (top)** Phil Geib/Encyclopædia Britannica Educational Corporation; **27 (bottom)** Jerome Gordon/Encyclopædia Britannica Educational Corporation; **28** Paul Tucker/Encyclopædia Britannica Educational Corporation; **29 (top)** Phil Geib/Encyclopædia Britannica Educational Corporation; **29 (bottom)** Jerome Gordon/Encyclopædia Britannica Educational Corporation; **31, 32, 33, 34, 36, 37** Phil Geib/Encyclopædia Britannica Educational Corporation.

Photographs

1 © Encyclopædia Britannica Educational Corporation; **13, 14** © (Robert Frerck)/Odyssey Productions/Chicago.